Food Hygi~~~ ~~~ations made ~~~~ ~~~~rs

A handbook for those working with food and drink

Compiled by

Food Solutions Publishing Ltd

Food Hygiene and Food Safety Regulations explained

www.food-solutions.org

Food Hygiene and Safety Regulations made easy for Food Handlers

A handbook for those working with food and drink

First published in 2010 by Food Solutions Publishing Ltd. Registered office: 164 Main Road, Goostrey, Cheshire, CW4 8JP.

www.food-solutions.org

Reprinted 2011

ISBN: 978-0-9557466-3-5

A CIP catalogue copy of this Handbook is available from the British Library

Executive Editor: Bob Salmon.

Assistant Editor: John Golton-Davis.

Administration: Jane Davies

Technical Support: Ian Moore

Cartoons: C. Foster

Printed in England by Think Digital Print Ltd, Oakham, Rutland.

Foreword

The people who eat the food you prepare at work rely on you. They don't just rely on you to make good and tasty food. They rely on you to keep it safe. Most food is safe, but sometimes things go wrong and that can make people ill. About a million people every year in the UK get food poisoning and about 500 of those people die.

You can keep food safe and help keep the people who eat the food you prepare healthy by using the advice in this handbook – it is easy to follow. It tells you how to check foods to make sure they're safe, how to handle food and equipment safely, and how to keep food cool to make sure it stays safe. It also tells you about keeping yourself and your workplace clean so you don't contaminate food.

If your job is to prepare food, the law says you are responsible for producing safe food. The same law applies across the whole of the European Union. The same food regulations apply whether you are preparing pizzas in Portsmouth or Paphos or Paris. It is up to you to comply with the regulations. The regulations themselves are very detailed, but, once you have been fully trained on hygiene and food safety and you follow the advice in this booklet you can be sure you're doing all the right things. You'll also find easy-to-follow practical advice in the Food Standards Agency's *Safer Food, Better Business* pack and DVD.

Keep food safe for everyone – it's what you'd expect from the people who prepare the food you eat.

Terrence Collis
Director of Communications, Food Standards Agency

Introduction

The European Community Food Hygiene Regulations affect everyone handling food, this includes charitable events (school fetes etc) in the UK. The way in which the regulations are written can be confusing. The idea of this handbook is to break down each regulation into simple steps.

Firstly – It is important to understand **why** the Regulations are needed. So the reasons why are explained.

Secondly – What does **the Regulation** actually say? If you are running or involved with a food business you need to know what is expected of you.

Thirdly – What this means to you. This is explained in plain English not jargon.

> **"You" may be the head chef, the cleaner, the waitress or the man come to fix the boiler. Each of you has equal responsibility to make sure the food is safe and risks are kept as small as possible**

Note

Texts of Regulations are correct as at the time of publication (February 2011). There may be amendments before the next edition. Food Solutions has produced an Ehandbook which is updated as and when changes to Regulations occur. See www.food-solutions.org

We would also recommend that you contact your Local Authority Environmental Health Department or professional advisor if you have any specific queries about your own business.

Most quotations in this handbook are taken from EC/852/2004 on the Hygiene of Foodstuffs. No attempt is made to interpret the law as only the Courts can do that.

Contents

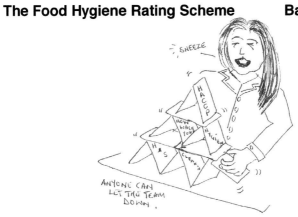

HACCP

Hazard Analysis and Critical Control Points

Why?

You will be told about HACCP but what does this mean? It means; identifying where **things can go wrong** (Critical Control Points), making checks at these points and doing the necessary **corrections to make sure that the food produced is safe.**

The origin of HACCP?

HACCP was developed by the Americans for their space programme. They did not want their astronauts to suffer tummy upsets through eating infected or contaminated food when in space.

Before HACCP was introduced food testing took place on the finished product. If the food was found to be infected or contaminated it would be too late as the food was already in space.

To overcome this, a system was devised to test food at stages of production (critical points). That meant that the risk of infection or contamination of the final product would be reduced to a minimum.

The system was so effective that it has now become part of international food regulations.

What is HACCP?

HACCP is about constant and consistent discipline in all stages of food production.

Take the example of making a ham sandwich.

Things that can go wrong:

1. The ingredients may be out of date.
2. The knife used may have been spreading peanut butter just before.
3. Raw chicken may have been dressed on the work surface.
4. The ham may not have been properly cooked.
5. The operator may have not washed his hands.

All these things could contaminate the sandwich. It would look right. It may even taste right. It could be <u>fatal to the consumer.</u>

The HACCP discipline looks at the risks at each stage. It identifies which risks could be serious and so be a hazard. It then creates the habits of making each risk as small as possible.

Corrections to make sure that the food produced is safe

1. Durability dates are checked.
2. Knives are cleaned.
3. Possible allergens are kept separate.
4. Work surfaces are cleaned properly.
5. Cooking temperatures are checked.
6. Hand washing becomes routine.

It is impossible to do away with all risks for all consumers. The HACCP system helps you control the risks so that the final product is as safe as it reasonably can be.

Summary:

In practice this means that all food handlers from importers to waiters must:

(a) Understand what risks and hazards to look out for within their own operation.

(b) Know the effects those risks might have on customers.

(c) Be able to identify places where things can go wrong (critical points) during the production of the product.

(d) Use the procedures put in place to reduce any risk to a minimum (you can never completely remove all risk).

(e) Check that everything is right according to the plans

(f) Be able to prove to the authorities that you have these procedures in place.

HACCP is the self control discipline that reminds you to do the right things at the right time. That way our ham sandwich will not end up being labelled as a jam sandwich.

All of the sections in this booklet are an important part of ensuring that your employer is complying with their responsibilities under the HACCP rules. As a food handler you must understand that YOU also must abide by the regulations.

Equipment

Why?

Equipment needs to be safe for the operator to use and easy to clean to avoid cross-contamination as well as doing the job it was bought for.

The regulation is:

All articles, fittings and equipment, with which food comes into contact, are to:
- *Be effectively cleaned and, where necessary, disinfected. Cleaning and disinfection are to take place at a frequency sufficient to avoid any risk of contamination.*

What this means is:

Contamination of foods comes from many sources. The main one is you. Other contamination comes from work surfaces, cloths, pests (like flies), the atmosphere and raw foods. It is essential to properly clean everything that may come into contact with foods.

General cleaning

It is important that you use the right product when cleaning.
- Detergents for washing off grease, fats and oils
- Clean cloths for wiping.
- Sanitiser or disinfectant, usually as a spray
- It is better to keep things clean than allow dirt to build up.

Make sure you fully understand what specific products are used where you work.

Procedures to follow

Hands; they need washing before you start work, after handling any raw foods, after a break or after using the toilet.

Avoid touching ready to eat foods if possible or use disposable gloves. Throw gloves away after each use.

Surfaces; wipe to remove any loose material. Then wash with hot water and a detergent, rinse and spray with a disinfectant before a final rinse and drying with a clean cloth. Observe contact times, some disinfectants need up to two minutes before rinsing away.

Utensils; should be cleaned as work surfaces remembering to remove all grease or charred material before starting to wash.

Equipment; should be regularly dismantled and food contact parts either put into a dishwasher or thoroughly cleaned as for surfaces. Avoid using scourers as they can make the surface rough. Rough surfaces cannot be cleaned easily and harbour bacteria (you will be given cleaning procedures for individual pieces of equipment separately).

Handles; these could be on doors, fridges, taps, cooker controls etc. These need regular cleaning, at least twice a day and certainly every time they have been touched by someone with dirty hands.

Spillages; wipe up directly and re-clean the surfaces, particularly after spills of raw foods.

Cutlery and plates; it is recommended that a dishwasher is used as this works at a higher temperature than your hands can bear. If not available, use the wash, disinfect, rinse, dry routine and avoid touching them with bare hands afterwards.

Key points:

> Make sure you know where stocks of cleaning materials are kept.
> Make sure you understand the company's cleaning procedure and policy.
> Cleaning materials are put back into the store when cleaning procedures are completed.
> If a cleaning material is running out or getting low tell your manager.
> Something may look clean, but it may be contaminated with bacteria.

Chopping boards

The main risk when using chopping boards is from bacterial contamination. This can be from raw foods (particularly poultry, fish and other raw meats), and hide in scratches on the board surface and from poor cleaning. Other risks are from contamination with allergenic foods (nuts, fish, shellfish, flour etc. see page 18), from taints (onions, garlic etc.).

Colour coding chopping boards helps to avoid cross contamination between different foods.
- Red-for fresh meat
- White- for ready-to-eat -foods
- Blue-for fish
- Green-for vegetables

The important thing is to keep them clean and stored correctly (preferably in a rack to separate). Tell your manager immediately if they become damaged.

General cleaning procedures

Background:

Contamination of foods comes from many sources. The main one is **you**. Other contamination comes from work surfaces, cloths, pests (like flies), the atmosphere, raw foods and packaging. It is essential to properly clean everything before it may come into contact with foods.

Preparation

It is important that you use the right product when cleaning.
- Detergents for washing off grease, fats and oils
- Clean cloths for wiping.
- Sanitiser or disinfectant, usually as a spray

In our premises we use the following

For hand washing	Name of product used
As a detergent	Name of product used
As a disinfectant	Name of product used
On floors	Name of product used
On work surfaces	Name of product used
In dish washers	Name of product used
Cloths for wiping	Name of product used
Cloths for drying	Name of product used

Procedure

Hands; these need washing before you start work, after handling any raw foods, after a break or using the toilet.

Avoid touching ready to eat foods if possible and use disposable non-latex gloves. Throw them away after each use.

Surfaces; wipe to remove any loose material. Then wash with hot water and a detergent, rinse and spray with a disinfectant before a final rinse and drying with a clean drying cloth. Observe contact times, some disinfectants need up to two minutes before rinsing away.

Utensils; should be cleaned as work surfaces remembering to remove all grease or charred material before starting to wash.

Equipment; should be regularly dismantled and food contact parts either put into a dishwasher or thoroughly cleaned as for surfaces. Avoid using scourers as they can make the surface rough. Rough surfaces cannot be cleaned easily and harbour bacteria (you will be given cleaning procedures for individual pieces of equipment separately).

Handles; these could be on doors, fridges, taps, cooker controls etc. these need regular cleaning, at least twice a day and certainly every time they have been touched by someone with dirty hands.

Spillages; wipe up directly and re-clean the surfaces, particularly after spills of raw foods.

Cutlery and plates; it is recommended that a dishwasher is used as this works at a higher temperature than your hands can bear. If not available, use the wash, disinfect, rinse, dry routine and avoid touching them with bare hands afterwards.

Key points:

- Stocks of cleaning materials are kept.

- Cleaning materials are put back into the store when cleaning procedures are completed.
- If a cleaning material is running out or getting low tell your manager.
- Do not mix cleaning materials. Mixtures may not work properly.
- **Allergens** - it is not just the kitchen area that should be wiped down to avoid cross-contamination of allergens, the tables and chairs used by customers also need to be kept clean.

  o Always thoroughly clean work surfaces before preparing a meal for someone who has a food allergy and make sure you do not use utensils like knives, spoons, probes or thermometers without washing them first.
  o Sanitisers and disinfectants do not destroy food allergens; however, detergent and hot water will usually remove most of the allergen.
  o When cleaning up spilt allergenic foods ensure that the discarded food is disposed of immediately so that it does not contaminate other foods or work surfaces

Traceability

Why?

If there is an ingredients scare that could be a cause of illness or even death amongst the general public your employer need to act quickly to:

1. Withdraw the food causing the problem as quickly as possible from sale.
2. Tell the authorities so that they can trace the original cause of the problem to enable it to be put right.

The regulation is:

The traceability of food, feed, food-producing animals, and any other substance intended to be, or expected to be, incorporated into a food or feed shall be established at all stages of production, processing and distribution. EC 178/2002 article 18.1

What this means is:

Your employer must have records of all foods coming in or going out to another business that can be shown to the authorities on demand.

This means your employer must:
1. Be able to supply details of where and when all raw materials were bought.
2. Be able to supply details of where and when food was sold, if to another business.

If your customers are the general public (the final consumer in a restaurant, shop etc), then the second point does not apply.

This regulation is very important – so please make sure you fully understand how your system works.

Personal Hygiene

Why?

Contamination from people can easily get into foods. Keeping food hygienic is important for the safety of the consumer and food quality.

The regulation is:

- *Every person working in a food-handling area is to maintain a high degree of personal cleanliness and is to wear suitable, clean and, where necessary, protective clothing.*
- *No person suffering from, or being a carrier of a disease likely to be transmitted through food or afflicted, for example, with infected wounds, skin infections, sores or diarrhoea is to be permitted to handle food or enter any food-handling area in any capacity, if there is any likelihood of direct or indirect contamination. Any person so affected and employed in a food business and who is likely to come into contact with food is to report immediately the illness or symptoms and, if possible, their causes to the food business operator.*

What this means is:

You must be fit for work. If you are suffering from:
- Diarrhoea or vomiting.
- Any other illness that could cause a problem with food safety e.g. a heavy cold.

You should report it to your manager and either stay at home or go straight home.

Key points:

➤ Always wear clean clothes when working with food.
➤ You should wear a hat when preparing food
➤ Your hair should be tied back.
➤ Watches and jewellery should not be worn when preparing food. The only exception is a plain wedding band.
➤ If you have piercings, these should be removed before entering any food preparation area. If they cannot be removed they should be covered with a brightly coloured waterproof plaster.
➤ If you cut yourself cover the cut with a brightly coloured waterproof plaster.
➤ You should not eat, smoke or chew gum when preparing food.
➤ Avoid touching your face or sneezing. If you do wash your hands immediately.

Hand Washing

DO NOT WASH YOUR HANDS IN SINKS USED FOR FOOD PREPARATION

Procedure:
1. Wet your hands with warm water.
2. Squirt liquid soap onto your palm. Rub your hands together to make lather.
3. Rub one hand along the back of the other with your fingers. Repeat with the other hand.
4. Rub in between your fingers, your thumbs and finger tips.
5. If there is any dirt under your finger nails use the nail brush to remove.
6. Rinse your hands with clean water.
7. When finished dry your hands thoroughly with a disposable towel.
8. Turn off the tap with the towel.
9. Dispose of the towel in the waste bin.

Key points:

> ➢ Regular washing of hands prevents harmful bacteria from spreading.
> ➢ If the soap dispenser runs out tell your manager.
> ➢ If the disposable towel dispenser runs out tell your manager.
> ➢ Food may not be safe if it is contaminated by germs, allergens or bits that should not be there. That is why you should wash your hands after handling raw meat, after going to the toilet or after touching a dirty door handle.

Best practice means
- Coloured plasters are used so that they show up if they fall off.
- Not wearing jewellery because (a) it can trap dirt (b) it might fall off into food.
- Wearing hats so that stray hairs do not get to where they should not be.

These rules are so that the food we produce is as safe as possible.

Allergens

Why?

When someone has a food allergy, eating even a small bit of that food can make them very ill. Some could even die. So, it's very important for you to take food allergy seriously.

The regulation is:

Food shall not be placed on the market, if it is considered to be unsafe.

Unsafe means either injurious to health or unfit. Some foods can harm the health of some people. This is called "allergenic reaction" and for them that food is injurious to health.
Under the Labelling Directive there is a legal duty to declare clearly on the label of pre-packed foods any allergen included in the ingredients.

What this means is:

1. Know what the allergens listed on page 20 are, what they look like and what foods they may be ingredients in.

2. Think about whether the food might be known by another name. For example, someone with an allergy to prawns might say that they have a crustacean allergy or a shellfish allergy. A person with a milk allergy cannot have something with lactose in it.

3. Make sure that you do not place allergenic material near other ingredients. Use the sealed containers provided.

4. Make sure you use separate knives, spoons, tongs, stirrers, meat thermometers etc when handling food with allergens in it.

5. Clean down thoroughly after using any one of allergenic ingredients.

6. If you are asked by a customer about allergenic ingredients, never guess. Don't be frightened to say you do not know. Check with your manager or the person who prepared the food before giving an answer.

7. If a meal is served by mistake which contains the allergenic food **NEVER SIMPLY REPLACE** the ingredient (see case study below).

8. Know the symptoms of an allergic reaction. Dial 999 and ask for an ambulance, with a paramedic. Say the person is having an anaphylactic reaction.

Symptoms to look out for:

   a. Tingling of the lips and itchy mouth/ throat.
   b. Difficulty breathing is a more common early symptom..
   c. Anaphylaxis also lowers blood pressure and the person my fall unconscious.
   d. A rash.

Key points:

> Read the booklet 'Food Allergy – what you have to do.
> Don't ever guess – always ask your manager or the person who prepared the food.
> Fully understand your company policy when you are given a Chef Card by a customer.

Case Study

A girl goes into a restaurant with friends. The set menu contains shell fish. She asks for Parma ham to be substituted as she was allergic to shell fish. The meal arrives with shell fish, the girl complains and the meal is returned to the kitchen. The chef, who was working under pressure, changes the shell fish for Parma ham, on the same plate.

THE GIRL HAD A SEVERE ALLERGIC REACTION AND DIED

Chef cards say:

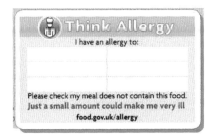

List of Allergens

Allergen	Often found in
Peanuts	Sauces, cakes, desserts, biscuits. *Peanuts are legumes, not nuts.*
Nuts	Almonds, hazelnuts, walnuts, Brazil nuts, cashews, pecans, pistachios, macadamia nuts and Queensland nuts. In sauces, desserts, ice cream, marzipan
Eggs	Mousses, sauces, pasta, quiche, mayonnaise
Milk	Yoghurt, cream, cheeses, cakes, biscuits
Crustaceans	Including: shrimps, prawns, crabs and lobsters, often in pastes
Fish	Pizzas, relishes, salad dressings, sauces
Sesame seeds	Breadsticks, tahini, houmous
Cereals containing Gluten	Including: wheat, spelt, rye, barley and oats in bread, sauces, and cakes.
Soya	In tofu, ice creams, vegetarian foods
Celery	Soups
Mustard	Salad dressings, soups, sauces, ham sandwiches, curries
Lupin	In some breads and pastries
Molluscs	Mussels etc
Sulphur dioxide/sulphites	Preservatives used in some foods and drinks, at levels above 10mg per kg or per litre in wines, beers, dried fruit.

Temperature Control

Why?

High enough temperature kills most bacteria. But it does not destroy the poisons (toxins) they might have produced. Low enough temperatures only slow bacteria from breeding. They will all be there ready to breed when the food warms up. Foods subject to bacteria must be kept below 8°C milk below 6°C and offal below 3°C. It is recommended that all perishable foods be kept between 2-5°C.

Regular maintenance of fridges is necessary to ensure that these temperatures are reached quickly and maintained.

The regulation is:

The Regulations specify that a cold chain should be maintained. This means that chilled product is not allowed to warm up and then be re-cooled or frozen.

Raw materials, ingredients, intermediate products and finished products likely to support the reproduction of pathogenic micro-organisms or the formation of toxins are not to be kept at temperatures that might result in a risk to health.
The cold chain is not to be interrupted. However, limited periods outside temperature control are permitted, to accommodate the practicalities of handling during preparation, transport, storage, display and service of food, provided that it does not result in a risk to health.

What this means is:

Key points:

> - High-risk meats have lower limits, 4C for poultry and 2C for minced meats. This latter must be frozen below -18C, which is the only frozen temperature specified in the EC legislation.
> - Milk must be below 8C, if it is to be collected every day, but below 6C, if collected on alternate days.
> - Large game must be chilled to 7C, although "chilling may not be necessary where climatic conditions permit".
> - Other meat must be brought into the cutting room progressively to ensure that it does not exceed 7C or 3C for offal.

<u>**Your employer will give you more instruction on this topic**</u>.

General points

Some foods obviously do not need chilling (sugar or salt). That is called ambient.

Eggs are usually displayed ambient with a recommendation to store chilled. The reason for this is that eggs bought chilled would attract condensation in transit. Any dampness on the shell could transmit contamination to the inside.

Some foods, like fresh soft fruits, can be damaged by freezing because ice crystals destroy their structure. These may be preserved in inert gases, which inhibit the growth of bacteria or over-ripening.

Cut surfaces of meats are almost invariably contaminated which is why special precautions must be applied to minced meats.

When cooking steaks the outside should be seared to reduce contamination. Where meat is cut there should be a supply of water above 82C for cleaning knives and equipment.

Foods held hot should be above 63C. Reheated foods should be "piping hot", except in Scotland where they must reach 82C (these are legal requirements).

What happens if hot held foods drop below 63C?

The Food Standards Agency recommends foods should not drop below 63C for longer than 2 hours. After that they should be chilled, quickly reheated or best discarded. Make sure you know your employer's policy.
Similarly, chilled foods could be displayed above 8C for one period of up to four hours. After that they must chilled below 8C until served, sold or discarded. Assess the risks. If it could be unsafe, discard. Ask your employer/supervisor if you are unsure.

You must be aware of the need to cook, re-heat and hold food safely. There are temperatures which food must reach both inside and out before being cooked properly. Ask your manager how to check.

You must also appreciate the need for proper thawing of frozen foods and rapid cooling of foods to be stored. If you are at all unsure ask your manager for further information.

Temperature probes are useful but may give false readings if not properly maintained. Clean boiling water should give a reading of 100C.

Health and Safety

Why?

This is a major topic and we can only give an outline summary here. The main provisions are in the Health and Safety at Work Act 1974 as amended and the following extracts are taken from that document. The H & S Executive has the responsibility of enforcing the legislation.

There are three main duties. They are for:
1. Employers to their employees.
2. Employers to visitors.
3. Employees to themselves and colleagues.

The regulation is:

1. *It shall be the duty of every employer to ensure, so far as is reasonably practicable, the health, safety and welfare at work of all his employees.*

2. *Without prejudice to the generality of an employer's duty under the preceding subsection, the matters to which that duty extends include in particular;*
   (a) *The provision and maintenance of plant and systems of work that are, so far as is reasonably practicable, safe and without risks to health.*
   (b) *Arrangements for ensuring, so far as is reasonably practicable, safety and absence of risks to health in connection with the use, handling, storage and transport of articles and substances.*
   (c) *The provision of such information, instruction, training and supervision as is necessary to ensure, so far as is reasonably practicable, the health and safety at work of his employees.*
   (d) *So far as is reasonably practicable as regards any place of work under the employer's control, the maintenance of it in a condition that is safe and without risks to health and the provision and maintenance of means of access to and egress from it that are safe and without such risks.*
   (e) *The provision and maintenance of a working environment for his employees that is, so far as is reasonably practicable, safe, without risks to health, and adequate as regards facilities and arrangements for their welfare at work.*

Except in such cases as may be prescribed, it shall be the duty of every employer to prepare and, as often as may be appropriate, revise a written statement of his general policy with respect to the health and safety at work of his employees and the organisation and arrangements for the time being in force for carrying out that policy, and to bring the statement and any revision of it to the notice of all his employees.

What this means for business operators is:

- If you have more than five employees, you must have a written policy statement.
- You must also be insured for at least £5 million and display the certificate.
- You should also have some posters on display as well as the no smoking signs.
- You will need to have emergency plans well developed and recorded. This will include evacuation of the premises, exits etc.
- You have to have a first aid kit readily available and checked regularly. One person at least should have some training and be designated first aider.
- You must report any accident at work if it results in three days off or any dangerous occurrences – where something happens that does not result in an injury, but could have done (near miss). Reporting is done on 0845 300 99 23.
- You must also have a record of every injury.
- Your manager must have done risk assessments for all aspects of the business.
- The risk assessment must take in premises. It must also look at any hazards to yourself, the other staff and any visitors.

What this means for other food handlers is:

- You should know where the first aid box is kept.
- You must recognise your responsibilities for your own and other people's safety.
- Read any posters or other literature provided by your employer about health and safety and act appropriately.
- Smoke only in designated areas.
- You should tell your manager if you or others have an accident.

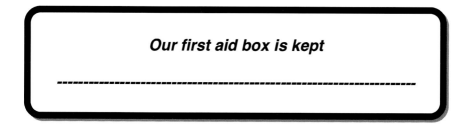

Our first aid box is kept

Why?

So that the customer knows what they are buying, what risks there may be and that they are not misled. They could be misled by the shape, packaging or setting in which the goods are displayed. At the moment the bulk of labelling regulations applies only to pre-packed foods. This is currently under review.

The regulation is:

Without prejudice to more specific provisions of food law, the labelling, advertising and presentation of food or feed, including their shape, appearance or packaging, the packaging materials used, the manner in which they are arranged and the setting in which they are displayed, and the information which is made available about them through whatever medium, shall not mislead the consumer.

What this means is:

You must be vigilant when dealing with perishable stock. **It is an offence to sell product after the "Use by" date** so you must always stick to your Company's policy for checking dates and for stock rotation. "Use by" is used for foods that may not be safe after the date. "Best before" is used for foods whose quality may suffer. "Sell by" and "Display until" have no legal force and are for guidance only.

Key points:

> - When stacking shelves bring the nearest to sell by date forward
> - Place fresh deliveries at the back.
> - Regularly check throughout the day to correct customer changes (check rotation of stock).
> - Check all products for durability dates daily.
> - Check for damaged packaging.
> - Goods which have passed their "Use by" dates or are damaged (e.g. seals broken, cracked eggs) must be placed in the designated container (your employer will tell you where this is).

Eggs. There are separate rules for selling eggs. You must always stick to your Company's policy for checking dates and for stock rotation.